FIRST SERIES OF
GRADED PIANOFORTE STUDIES

Grade 3

ABRSM

FIRST SERIES
GRADED PIANOFORTE STUDIES
GRADE 3

The thumb as soloist

GURLITT

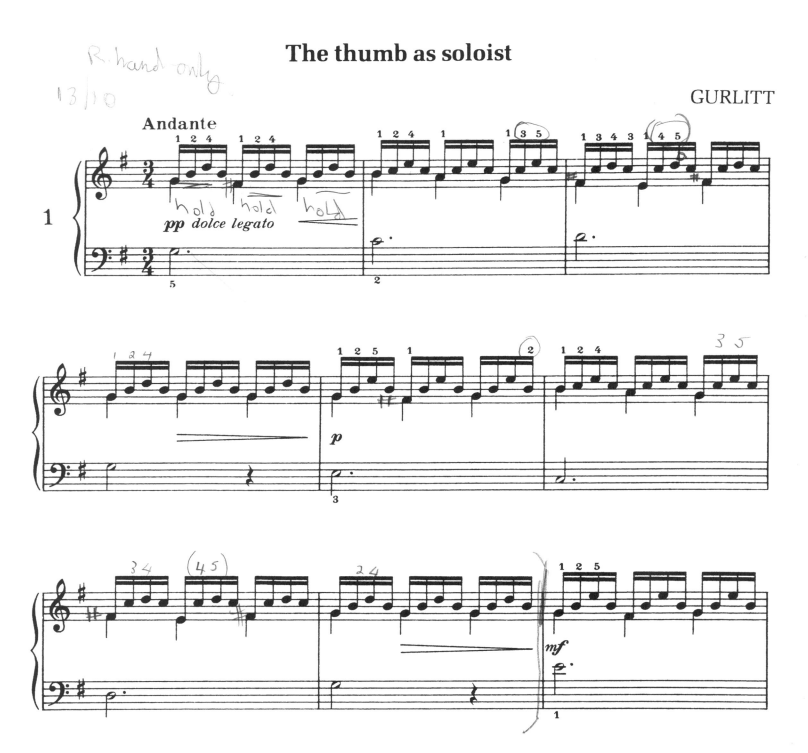

Published by ABRSM (Publishing) Ltd, a wholly owned subsidiary of ABRSM
Copyright, 1934, by The Associated Board of the Royal Schools of Music

A.B. 535

Syncopation

STAMATY, Op.37 No.12

Tone gradation and evenness of note successions

HENNES

Speed and steadiness

KÖHLER, Op.63 No.1

Turning the fore-arm easily

BERTINI, Op.100 No.13

Avoiding continuous thumb pressure

DUVERNOY

Phrasing and slurs

MAYER, Op.340 No.2

Finger fluency

LE COUPPEY, Op.20 No.15

8

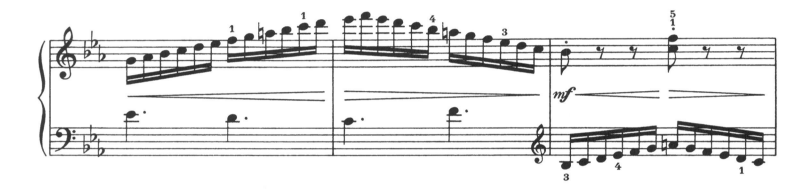

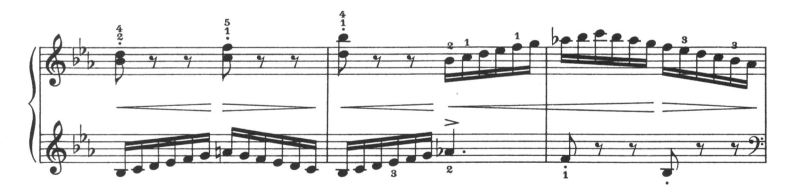

Finger control

KÖHLER

Playing two melodies together

F. WOHLFAHRT, from Op.36

Contrasts of tone quality

BERTINI, Op.29 No.18

* For small hands here omit the higher note in each octave.

Tied notes

LEMOINE, Op.37 No.38

Double notes

BURGMÜLLER, Op.100 No.4

Using the thumb lightly

LOESCHHORN, Op.65 No.47

Slurs and key-rebound

STAMATY, Op. 38 No. 2

Allegro moderato

15

Broken chords

BERENS

Semitones

GURLITT, Op.82 No.99

Turning the fore-arm freely and swiftly

LEMOINE, Op.37 No.40

Printed in England by Caligraving Limited Thetford Norfolk

A.B. 535

4:10